FIRE IN YOUR HOME

Prevention & Survival

NFPA No. SPP-52B
Library of Congress No. 78-60515
ISBN 0-87765-131-0

Batterymarch Park, Quincy, Massachusetts 02269-9101

Table of Contents

CHAPTER

Fire!

"Our house is on fire!"

If you think it will never happen to you, consider this:

Every year, almost 4,700 Americans die in home fires. That's 13 people every day, dying in their own homes.

In addition to the deaths, thousands of people severely burned in fires face disfigurement and pain. Severe burns often mean a hospital stay of several weeks, followed by months or years of therapy.

It's real, it does happen, and it could happen to you.

It's real, it does happen, and it could happen to you. Nothing can bring back your family and loved ones if fire takes them. But the information in this book and the simple actions it recommends could save most of the thousands of people who will die in home fires this year.

If you read and follow the suggestions in this book, you will have three strong defenses against fire:

1. You will be better able to keep fire out of your home.
2. If fire does strike, your family will have an early warning.
3. You will have an escape plan that can save your lives.

The information that follows comes from the nation's top firesafety experts at the National Fire Protection Association. The recommendations have been proven in real fires. They do save lives. They could save yours.

Before we get to specific recommendations, you should know the enemy. You should know how fire happens and how it kills.

Fire Basics

For a fire to start, three elements must be present: oxygen, fuel and heat. In a fire, these combine in a self-sustaining chain reaction.

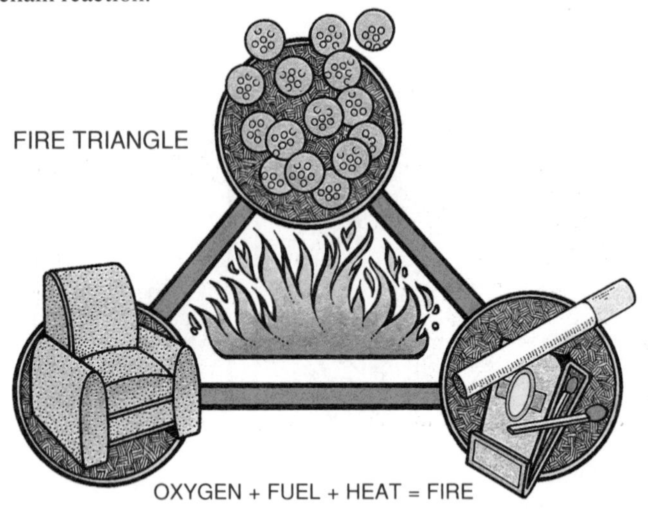

Most fires start when some man-made device supplies the missing ingredient, heat.

Oxygen is all around us, and almost any material can become fuel for a fire: clothes, furniture, plastics, flammable liquids, wood. Most fires start when some man-made device supplies the missing ingredient, heat.

When a fire starts burning, it quickly makes your home a deadly place. Fire consumes the oxygen, feeding itself, suffocating you. Normal air is about 21 percent oxygen; but during a fire, the oxygen level rapidly drops. If it falls below 17 percent, clear thinking and muscle control become difficult, and attempts to escape become irrational. For example, you might claw at the door rather than simply turn the knob. When

oxygen falls within the range of 10 to 6 percent, breathing stops. After 4 to 6 minutes without oxygen, brain death occurs.

Fire also produces superheated air and smoke containing poisonous gases; these fire products can kill you long before the flames reach you.

It may surprise you to learn that few fire victims are burned. Most die from inhaling smoke's poisonous gases, which work silently and quickly. If fire hits your home, you may never wake up. If you do wake up, poisonous gases may still knock you out when you stand up.

Toxic gases work in different ways, all of them deadly:

Carbon monoxide prevents oxygen from reaching the brain. Invisible and odorless, it is the most abundant of fire gases, produced in all fires.

Carbon dioxide forces you to breathe faster, increasing your intake of other poisonous gases.

Hydrogen sulfide affects the nervous system, causing dizziness and pain in the respiratory system.

Nitrogen dioxide is extremely toxic. It numbs the throat and can interfere with breathing.

In addition to these gases, smoke contains particles that irritate the respiratory system, impair sight and cause coughing and sneezing. Smoke moves fast, restricting visibility, obscuring light. Surrounded by smoke, you will have difficulty breathing, seeing or thinking clearly.

Surrounded by smoke, you will have difficulty breathing, seeing or thinking clearly.

While smoke is at work, fire's heat also overwhelms human tolerance. Our bodies can bear temperatures between 150 and 200 degrees for only a short time. Superheated air and gases cause loss of consciousness or death within minutes.

Read On!

To survive a fire in your home, you must have warning, you must know what to do, and you must move quickly. The chapters of this book provide the information you need. But all the information in the world will not help unless you act on it.

Start to protect yourself and your family today. Read this book. Then follow its recommendations so you will be ready if fire strikes your home.

CHAPTER

2

Smoke Detectors: Buying Time

Most fatal home fires strike at night, while people are asleep. So every home needs smoke detectors to wake people up before smoke overcomes them.

Fire officials consider smoke detectors the most effective low-cost firesafety devices you can buy. Almost every day, a smoke detector saves somebody's life. In fact, years of real-life experience show that with working smoke detectors, your risk of dying in a fire is cut in half!

Later chapters will show you how to escape from a fire, but no amount of planning and practice will save you if you never wake up. The smoke detector is your first line of defense, to wake you up in time to escape.

The smoke detector is your first line of defense, to wake you up in time to escape.

What to buy

Dozens of reputable brands of smoke detectors are readily available. No matter where you buy your detectors and regardless of what type they are, be sure to buy only "labeled" units— those bearing the mark of an organization that tests and evaluates products. Any labeled smoke detector — whether a photoelectric or ionization device, powered by batteries or household current — offers adequate protection.

To get the protection you paid for, however, you must follow the manufacturer's recommendations for installation, testing and maintenance.

How many do you need?

Minimum protection requires smoke detectors outside each bedroom and on each additional level of the house— including the basement.

The chance of a fire starting in a bedroom is small, unless someone makes a habit of smoking in bed. (One of the primary rules for preventing fires is: *Never smoke in bed.*) If anyone in your household does smoke in their bedroom, or if you have other reasons to be concerned about fire starting there, install an *additional* detector in the bedroom. But this does not replace the smoke detector needed outside the bedroom door.

Most home fires start in living areas— the den, family room or living room. On a floor with no bedrooms, install the required detector in or near the living area.

For extra protection, you should also install detectors in the dining room, furnace room, utility room and hallways.

Smoke detectors are not usually recommended for kitchens, attics (finished or unfinished) or garages. You can increase your protection, though, by installing heat detectors in these areas. But you should not substitute heat detectors for the smoke detectors we have recommended above.

At least two-thirds of home fire deaths are caused by inhalation of smoke, with its poisonous gases. The smoke of a fire will trigger your smoke detector — if it is properly installed and maintained — and give you time to escape.

The smoke of a fire will trigger your smoke detector — if it is properly installed and maintained — and give you time to escape.

Installing smoke detectors

To install most smoke detectors, all you need are a screw-driver and a drill. Follow the manufacturer's installation instructions.

Smoke detectors operate either on batteries or household current. A detector that plugs into a wall outlet must have a restraining device so that the plug cannot accidentally be pulled from the wall. Detectors can also be hard-wired into the electrical system, but never hard-wire a detector to a circuit that can be turned off at a wall switch.

Because smoke rises, each detector should be mounted high on a wall or on the ceiling to detect the first traces of smoke.

- For a wall-mounted unit, the top of the detector should be 4 to 12 inches from the ceiling.
- A ceiling-mounted detector should be placed at least 4 inches from any wall.
- In a room with a high pitched ceiling, mount the detector on or near the ceiling's highest point.
- If a stairway leads to an upper story, install the detector in the path where smoke would travel up the stairs.

Make sure that people in the bedrooms can hear and recognize the sound of the detector, even with the doors closed.

- Don't install a detector near a window, door or air register where drafts could reduce its sensitivity.
- Locate a basement smoke detector close to the stairway leading to the floor above. But don't install the detector at the top of the basement stairs; dead air space near the door may prevent smoke from reaching the detector.

Most important, make sure that people in the bedrooms can hear and recognize the sound of the detector, even with the doors closed.

If you have any questions, ask your local fire department. A member of the department will be glad to advise you on the best placement of your detector.

Keep your smoke detectors working!

Recent surveys have shown that while millions of homes have smoke detectors, more than one-third of those detectors are not in good working order. These endanger their owners by creating a false sense of security.

It's extremely important to test and clean all detectors regularly. Replace the batteries according to the manufacturer's recommendations or at least once a year. Warn everyone in your household to leave working batteries in smoke detectors — resist the temptation to borrow them for other purposes.

Test your smoke detectors once a week to make sure you're protected. Follow the manufacturer's instructions for testing. It only takes a moment to test a smoke detector that could save your life.

Test your smoke detectors once a week to make sure you're protected.

Clean your detectors at least twice a year to remove cobwebs and dust that can impair a detector's sensitivity. If you repaint a room, make sure no paint gets on the smoke detector.

Properly installed and maintained, smoke detectors can warn you in time to escape. The following chapters will tell you how to make sure you're ready to heed that warning.

CHAPTER

3

Meet EDITH

If you have planned and practiced for the worst possible conditions, you won't waste precious moments figuring out how to escape.

Your smoke detector can give you extra time in case of fire. But when the smoke detector awakens you, what will you do? What will your children do?

You'll all know what to do if you have planned and practiced an escape. Each member of the family must know how to act and where to go in a fire, because escape may not be as easy as walking out the door.

If you have planned and practiced for the worst possible conditions, you won't waste precious moments figuring out how to escape. You'll already know.

Talking about your escape plan is not enough: you have to practice it. The more you practice, the better the chance that your family will act from practice, not from panic.

Now introduce yourself to EDITH.

EDITH stands for Exit Drills In The Home. EDITH is a method for quickly formulating your family's escape plan.

1. List all possible escape routes from your home.

Fire is unpredictable. Your first or even your second escape route may be blocked. The more escape routes you have, the better.

____

____

____

____

Can each escape route really be used in an emergency? Try them. Can children unlock and open the windows? Are hallways clear of clutter?

2. Locate two escape routes from each bedroom.

Usually the alternate escape route from each bedroom will be a window. It must not be painted shut or blocked by a screwed-on screen.

Don't guess. Assess each route realistically. Be sure you and your family can get out by every escape route you've planned. Be sure everyone can reach and operate the latches, bolts, locks, and chains.

In a two-story house, plan your escape through a window onto an adjacent roof or porch. If you have no alternative, and you must use an escape ladder, be sure everyone knows how to use it. Make sure it is labeled and listed by a testing laboratory.

Be sure everyone can reach and operate the latches, bolts, locks, and chains.

3. **Draw a floor plan of your home.**

Even if you know every nook and cranny of your home, you should use the grid sheet in the back of this book to draw a floor plan of your home. The floor plan will show you all possible escape routes at a glance. You can hang it on a bulletin board along with the fire department phone number to alert babysitters and other visitors about the escape routes.

4. **Include all windows, doors and outdoor features in your floor plan.**

Remember to mark every outdoor feature and all possible obstacles. Can you climb out on a roof or balcony? Is there a tree that can be reached from a window? Try each of these outside aids to be sure they can be reached and can support the weight of an adult.

5. **On your floor plan, indicate primary and alternate escape routes from each room.**

Usually the door will be the primary exit from a bedroom; a window will be the alternate.

Each person must understand that if the first exit seems dangerous, he must immediately use the second escape route. The next chapter describes how to test a door to see if the way is clear.

Once out of the house, no one goes back in for any reason, until the fire department says it's safe.

6. **Designate a meeting place outside and mark it on your floor plan.**

Choose a spot that everyone will remember. Use the front of the house if you can; that's where the fire department will arrive.

Really hammer this home: *once out of the house, no one goes back in for any reason, until the fire department says it's safe.*

While you are checking out your meeting place, look to see that your house number is displayed in large, contrasting numerals your fire department can easily see.

7. **Locate a fire alarm box or a neighbor's house for calling the fire department.**

Include this on the floor plan, along with the fire department's number and the street address of your home. Tape the fire department's number to the phones in your house so it will be ready if a neighbor needs to call.

8. **Go over the entire plan with every member of your family.**

Discuss the floor plan and explain each escape route. Walk through the escape routes for each room with the entire family. Use this walk-through to double check your escape routes.

Have your children practice saying the fire department phone number, the family name, the street address and town, as they would if calling the fire department. Make sure they understand they should run to a neighbor's house to make this call.

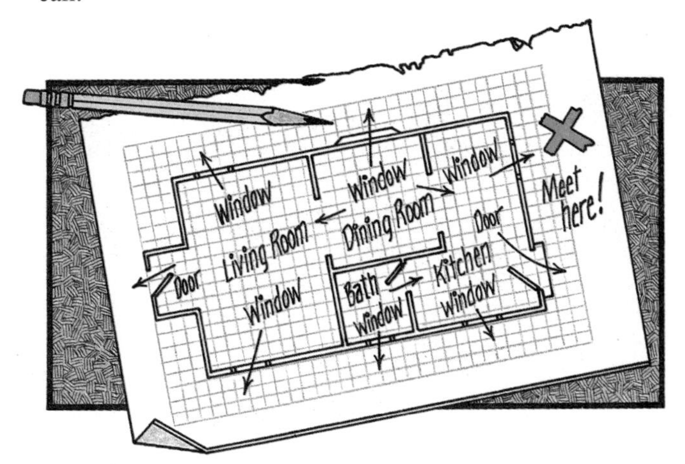

9. Train every child in your home to follow the plan.

Children are frightened in fire. All too often, their bodies are found after a fire in places where they tried to hide. So teach your children, even the very young, that they can't hide from fire: they must escape from it.

The more times children have taken part in a fire drill, the better the chance they will react correctly to a real fire.

The more times children have taken part in a fire drill, the better the chance they will react correctly to a real fire.

You may decide it's best for a very young child to stay in his room until you come to get him. But what if you are trapped or find the path to the child's room blocked? As early as possible, each child must be taught how to escape alone.

10. Go over the entire plan with a representative from your local fire department.

In most cities and towns, you can do this in your home while the fire fighter makes a simple firesafety check. Get the professional's advice on your escape plan and change it as suggested. Be sure to point out an infant's room or the room of an elderly person or a person with a disability that may impede his or her escape.

11. Hold a fire drill at least once every six months.

Make the drill as realistic as possible. Don't announce it in advance.

In a real fire, you must be prepared to move quickly, carefully, without panic. Don't let your fire drill become a race; make sure everyone knows exactly what to do.

Vary the drill by calling out different hazards and different kinds of fires. One drill, for example, might place the fire in the kitchen, while another puts it in the family room. Does everyone understand how the fire's location affects their escape routes?

At the beginning you may want to stay back and coach your children, being sure that they check for all the hazards you described to them. But the goal is for children to get out without assistance.

Drills not only give you practice, they also keep your escape plan up to date. Don't hesitate to change your plan as people's needs and abilities change.

CHAPTER

4

Survival

You awaken to the sound of your smoke detector. You're still groggy. Are you just sleepy? ...or are you already inhaling small amounts of poisonous gas from the fire?

Fortunately, you and your family have planned and practiced your escape routes. Now your survival may depend on your ability to handle the situation, calmly and deliberately. It isn't easy.

Fire is unpredictable. Though your smoke detector should sound an early warning, and your escape plan should give you a clear escape route, you must be ready for the unexpected. You must know what dangers to look for and how to handle them. Study the following survival tips and explain them to your family as you discuss and practice your escape plan.

You must know what dangers to look for and how to handle them.

1. Sleep with the bedroom doors closed. The closed door offers protection against heat and smoke. Even a light weight hollow core door may delay the fire, giving you extra time to escape. You may argue that you want to be able to hear your children. But consider this: closed doors can impede the spread of fire into your bedroom and theirs, giving all of you precious extra time to escape.

For the same reason, as you make your way along your escape route, you should close every door behind you.

2. Be sure everyone recognizes the sound of the smoke detector and knows that it means "Get out now!" If you have not yet held a fire drill, you must make sure your whole family recognizes the sound of the smoke detector. Just in case, shout a warning like "Fire, everyone outside!"

3. Do not waste time getting dressed or gathering valuables. You have no time to spare. You can borrow clothes later, and no possession is worth your life.

Put the back of your hand against the crack between the door and the door frame, on the side with the hinges.

4. Feel every door before you open it. Stay low in case smoke or toxic fumes are seeping around the door. Kneel or crouch at the door, reach high, and put the back of your hand against the crack between the door and the door frame, on the side with the hinges.

If the door is hot, there is danger on the other side. Do not open the door: use your second way out.

Even if the door is cool, open it carefully. A fire that has died down for lack of oxygen may flare up when the door opens. Brace your shoulder against the door and open it *slowly*. If heat and smoke come in, slam the door and make sure it is latched. Use your alternate escape route.

If the hall is clear of smoke and fire, proceed carefully; your usual exit may be safe. As you go, remember to close every door behind you.

5. Use windows for escape and rescue. If your primary escape route through the door is unsafe, you will have to use the second way out — usually a window — to escape the fire.

First make sure the door is tightly closed. Otherwise, the draft from the open window may draw smoke and fire into the room.

If you are on the first or second floor, you can probably drop to the ground from your window. Moving a chair to the window may make it easier to climb out. Go out feet first, on your stomach. Hold on to the sill with both hands, lowering yourself as far as possible. Then drop to the ground, bending your knees to cushion the landing.

You can lower small children from the window. If there are people outside, they can help break the fall. If not, lower the child as far as possible and let him drop. Do not go out first and expect young children to follow you. If they panic, you will have no way of helping them once you're on the ground.

If your window is more than two stories off the ground, you should not jump. Unless you have a balcony, a porch or garage roof or a tree to climb down, wait at the window for the fire department. Open the window a few inches at the top and the bottom, so that fresh air can enter from the lower opening and smoke can leave through the upper portion. If you see that the window is drawing smoke in, close it immediately.

Stay at the window and wave a light-colored towel, sheet or other signal to help the fire department locate you. If there is a phone in the room, call the fire department and tell the dispatcher where you are. This information will be relayed to the fire fighters on the scene.

6. If you must go through smoke, crawl under it on your hands and knees. Do not stand up. In a serious fire, superheated air, as hot as 1000 degrees F, will rise to the ceiling. Below that, but still near the ceiling, is a thick layer of smoke containing deadly carbon monoxide.

If you see smoke, crawl on your hands and knees. Do not crawl on your belly, because some heavier toxic gases will settle in a thin layer on the floor. Crawling on your hands and knees keeps your head in a safety zone from about a foot off the floor to doorknob height.

If you see smoke, crawl on your hands and knees. Do not crawl on your belly.

7. If your clothes catch fire: Stop, drop and roll. The moment your clothes start to burn, stop where you are. Do not run. Drop to the ground and cover your face and mouth with your hands to protect them from the flames. Roll over and over to smother the flames.

Have children and adults in your family practice this procedure. Make sure they know they should never run if their clothes are on fire. Running just gives the flames more oxygen.

Also tell your family how to help if someone else's clothes catch fire. Tackle the person or knock him down and make him roll on the ground. If possible, throw a blanket or rug over the victim to smother the fire.

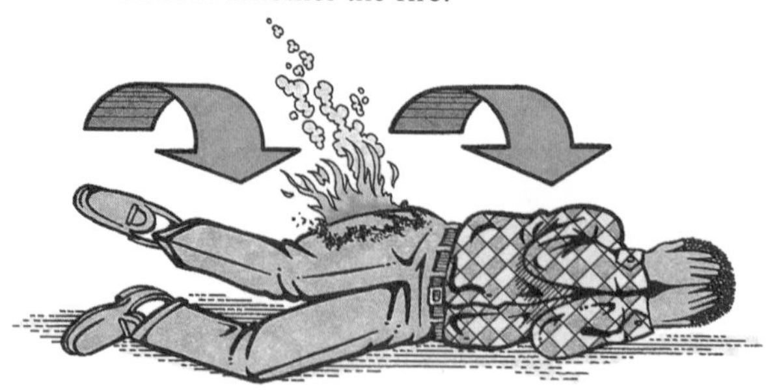

If someone is inside, a trained fire fighter has the best chance of a successful rescue.

8. Once you are out of the burning house, go immediately to your meeting place. Do not go back in for any reason.

At the meeting place, check to see if anyone is still inside so fire fighters can be told when they arrive. If someone is inside, a trained fire fighter with protective clothing and breathing apparatus has the best chance of a successful rescue.

9. Call the fire department from a neighbor's phone. It is too dangerous to call from the burning house.

Give the full address first. Fire trucks will be on their way while you give the dispatcher full information about any people trapped inside. Stay calm and stay on the phone until you have answered all questions.

If you use a fire alarm pull box, stay there until the fire fighters arrive, and guide them to the fire.

10. Don't let anyone go back into the building. Others may be tempted to try to save trapped family members, or even pets or favorite possessions. Keep a firm grip on small children. The risk is too high.

11. Get medical attention for burns. If someone gets burned, don't put ice or butter or ointments on the injury. Immediately cool the burn with cold tap water to stop the heat injury, then get the victim to a doctor or hospital. Delay may worsen the injury.

Stay calm... stay alive.

Fire and smoke are a deadly combination requiring calm, deliberate action. Preparation is the key to staying calm and in control. Your smoke detector will give you time to follow the escape routes you've planned and practiced. By staying calm, you'll be able to deal with unexpected dangers along the way.

In the following chapter, we will discuss special situations that affect your escape planning.

Preparation is the key to staying calm and in control.

CHAPTER

5

Special Plans for Special Cases

The safest location for the bedroom of a person with a disability is on the ground floor, with a door leading directly to the outside.

The elderly and people with disabilities

Elderly people and people with disabilities that may impede their escape from a fire should have smoke detectors inside their rooms, in addition to the smoke detectors recommended in Chapter 2. It's a good idea to install a telephone in the room as well, and to display on the phone the emergency numbers for fire, police and ambulance assistance.

The safest location for the bedroom of a person with a disability is on the ground floor, with a door leading directly to the outside. If the bedroom must be on the second floor, work out a special escape plan.

Be sure the fire department knows that the occupants of the house include a person who may have difficulty escaping a fire. Mention this when you go over your escape plan with a fire department representative.

Young children

In case of a fire, you may not be able to reach your children. They must, therefore, understand how to escape from fire on their own. During exit drills and discussions about escaping from fire, stress your confidence that they can get out on their own, and have them practice doing it.

While children under three years old should be part of your family's exit drills, they may not be able to escape a fire on their own. If possible, their bedrooms should adjoin the room of their parents or an older child, preferably with a connecting door.

Apartments

If you live in an apartment, there are special guidelines you should follow in addition to the survival points in Chapter 4.

In drawing your escape plan, mark the location of the nearest fire alarm pull box. This will allow you to warn other residents about the fire as you are making your escape. If there is no fire alarm pull box, you can warn your neighbors by shouting and pounding on the apartment doors as you escape from the building. Leave the full evacuation of the building to the fire department.

Never use an elevator in case of a fire. Heat and smoke could kill you if the elevator stops on the floor where the fire is burning.

Never use an elevator in case of a fire. Heat and smoke could kill you if the elevator stops on the floor where the fire is burning.

If fire blocks your exit, close your apartment door and cover all cracks where smoke could enter. If your apartment is two stories or more above the ground, do not jump from your window. Telephone the fire department, even if fire fighters are already on the scene, and tell them where you are trapped. Don't hang up the phone until the dispatcher has all the information. In addition, wave a sheet or towel from the window to help fire fighters find you.

While waiting for rescuers, you can draw fresh air in and let smoke out by opening a window at the top and the bottom. Be ready to close the window quickly if smoke is drawn in.

Firesafety Tips

1. Keep attic free from combustibles such as old newspapers or magazines, etc.
2. Install smoke detectors on each level of the home.
3. Always use a fireplace screen.
4. Never overload electrical outlets.
5. Never store gasoline inside the home.
6. Store matches and lighters out of the reach of small children.
7. Have your chimney and heating system inspected annually.
8. Store paints, thinners and other flammables in original containers, away from heat, sparks or flame.
9. Practice firesafety when cooking.
10. Never smoke in bed.
11. Display large house numbers that the fire department can easily see.
12. Be sure all smoking materials are fully extinguished and disposed of carefully.
13. Take extra care in heating your home -- particularly if space heaters are being used.
14. Make sure there are two clear ways out of every room.

SMOKE
GAS
0322

Mobile homes

If you live in a mobile home, follow the same procedures that apply to conventional dwellings. In addition, your gas-fired appliances pose a special fire hazard. Be sure that gas heaters are vented to the outside, and that LP gas tanks are never stored inside your home. Keep all exits clear, and install smoke detectors on interior walls.

Babysitters

Make it clear that your only concern is to get everyone out of the house quickly and safely.

Even when you're not home, your fire escape plan can still protect your family, if you take time to explain the plan to your babysitter. Show the babysitter your floor plan with escape routes marked, and point out the telephone number of the fire department. In the back of this book is a Babysitter Checklist to use as a quick reference for the babysitter. Always leave the phone number where you can be reached in case of emergency.

When you explain your family's firesafety plans to your babysitter, make it clear that your only concern is to get everyone out of the house quickly and safely. If the alarm sounds, no one should try to find the fire, much less try to put it out. No one should waste time gathering belongings.

Pets

If you own pets, you may have noticed that animals were not included in the escape plan. This is intentional. A serious fire is so dangerous that you simply do not have time to consider anything but saving human lives. Do not take the risk of trying to bring a pet with you.

Dogs and cats, acting on their natural fear of fire, will often escape on their own, even before you do, and may join you when you gather at your meeting place.

If a pet remains trapped inside, tell the fire fighters where they might find it.

No one in your family should ever return to a burning house to find a pet. This may be difficult to explain to a child, but the alternative is far, far worse.

Now you are armed with a lot of information on escaping from a fire. The next two chapters go one step better: they help you prevent a fire from happening in your home.

CHAPTER

6

Learn Not To Burn®

Even with smoke detectors, an escape plan, and provisions for special situations, you have no guarantee of surviving a fire in your home.

It's far better to keep fire from happening in the first place. You can do this if you and your family "learn not to burn."®

This chapter and the next cover many examples of fire hazards, chosen because fires *do* start in these ways. Beyond recognizing these hazards, though, you should cultivate the habit of being alert to any situation where fuel and heat may come together to start a fire in your home.

First, let's look at the major causes of home fires.

1. Carelessness with smoking materials

This is the single largest cause of fatal home fires. If you smoke, always use large, heavy ashtrays and don't let them become so full that hot ashes might spill over the side. Empty the ashtrays only when they have had time to cool completely, and check to make sure nothing is burning.

Before you go to bed after a party, check for smoldering cigarettes under cushions of couches and chairs. A cigarette that falls into an upholstered chair can smolder for hours before bursting into flame.

2. Children playing with matches

Children are fascinated by fire. Until they're taught or suffer a painful experience, they don't understand the danger of fire.

Make sure your children learn the basics of firesafety. Learning can be fun, but make sure they do learn. Especially critical is the lesson that matches and lighters are tools for adults to use, not toys for children to play with.

In addition, keep matches and lighters out of children's reach. That means keeping them out of the "strike zone," from the floor to the highest point your child can reach — about adult shoulder height.

Include all your children in your escape planning and drills, and have them participate in your safety inspection of your home (see Chapter 7). Then, when your children are old enough, teach them how to use matches and lighters safely.

Include all your children in your escape planning and drills.

3. Carelessness with cooking and heating appliances

Heating and cooking equipment account for a larger number of home fires than any other cause.

Have your heating system professionally inspected once a year, and any other time you suspect a problem.

If you have a coal or wood-burning stove, check with the fire department to make sure it is installed properly, and is at a safe distance from combustibles. Clothes, furniture and newspapers should be kept well away from stoves, fireplaces and space heaters.

In fireplaces and wood stoves, use well-seasoned wood. Green wood burns inefficiently and forms creosote on chimney walls — fuel for dangerous chimney fires. To reduce the risk of chimney fires, keep your fire a moderate size, and never use your stove or fireplace to burn trash, which may send burning fragments up the chimney. Use a fireplace screen to keep sparks from flying into the room.

Allow ashes to cool before disposing of them in a tightly covered metal container, not in boxes or bags.

In the kitchen, be alert to your cooking habits. Stove burners and ovens can inflict severe burns or start fires. Be attentive, and practice these safety tips:

- Never leave your cooking unattended, and never leave potholders on the stove.
- Do not store things over the stove, where someone may be burned while reaching for them.
- Wear short or close-fitting sleeves when cooking; loose clothing can catch fire.
- To reduce the risk of kitchen fires, keep your stove and oven clean.
- Turn pot handles in so they can't get knocked off the stove or pulled down by small children. Make sure your children understand that they can be severely burned if they tip over a pot or an electrical appliance like a coffeepot.
- Also teach your children that hot liquids can cause painful burns. An adult should test bathwater before a child gets into the tub. (You can reduce the danger of burns by lowering the temperature setting on your water heater to 120 degrees.)

If a grease fire should start in your kitchen, smother the flames by covering the pan with a lid or a larger pan, and turn off the burner. Never pour water on a grease fire.

In case of an oven fire, close the oven door and turn off the oven. Use the same technique if a fire starts in a microwave oven: push the stop button and leave the door closed until the fire is out.

If you're not sure what load your circuits are designed for, have an electrician check out your electrical system.

4. Faulty electrical wiring

Don't overload electrical outlets. Most outlets have two receptacles, and only one appliance should be plugged into any receptacle at a time. Special appliances, such as air conditioners and large space heaters, should have their own heavy-duty electrical circuits. If you're not sure what load your circuits are designed for, have an electrician check out your electrical system.

If a fuse blows in your home, try to find out why it blew before you replace it. Make sure the new fuse is the right size and amperage. Fuses protect you against electrical fires; you endanger yourself if you misuse them.

Misused extension cords are a common fire hazard. Plug only one appliance into an extension cord. Don't run extension cords under rugs or across doorways, and never hang them over nails— the insulation could deteriorate, exposing a live wire. If you regularly use extension cords, consider having additional circuits installed.

Prevent electrical shocks. If there are small children in your home, insert plastic child-protector covers into outlets. Make sure everybody in your family knows they should not use a hair dryer or similar appliance when their hands are wet or when they are standing in water. Unplug appliances after use; and if the inside of an appliance gets wet, have it professionally serviced before using it again.

5. Faulty electrical fixtures

Check electrical cords for cracks, fraying, broken plugs and loose connections. Cords showing these danger signs should be replaced, along with any cord or plug that gets hot when it is in use. If you buy an old lamp from a garage sale or thrift shop, play it safe: have it rewired before you use it.

Lamps that fall over easily are fire hazards, as are lampshades that are too close to bulbs. Look for labels on fixtures showing the maximum wattage, and do not use a larger bulb.

As a general rule, if appliances or fixtures aren't working right, have them repaired by a professional before you use them.

6. Open flames

Use candles or oil-burning lamps only if their holders are stable and in good condition. If you are leaving a room for more than a few moments, extinguish all flames; and never leave a child alone with an open flame, even briefly.

In case the electrical power goes out, keep flashlights ready: using candles in an emergency could be dangerous.

Never smoke when you work with flammable liquids.

7. Flammable liquids

All flammable liquids present a fire hazard, because their vapors can be ignited so easily. Gasoline vapors, for example, can be ignited by a single spark. Even ordinary nail polish is a flammable liquid.

Don't take chances. Never smoke when you work with flammable liquids, and don't use or store them near any source of heat, spark or flame. Remember that many spray can products, like paint and hair spray, are flammable liquids held under pressure. Use these carefully, away from heat or flame, and follow the directions when you dispose of them.

If you must keep a small amount of gasoline on hand for a lawnmower or similar equipment, never store it in the house. Store it in a garage or shed in a safety can, one with a spring closure valve, vapor vent, pour spout and the label of a testing laboratory. Use that same shed or garage for storing paint and other flammable liquids, in tight, labelled metal containers. It's dangerous to store any flammable liquid in a glass jug, discarded bleach bottle, or other makeshift container. Either use the original container, or dispose of the flammable liquid.

8. Faulty chimneys and vents

Have chimneys and fireplaces inspected annually for cracks, crumbling bricks, obstructions and accumulated creosote. If the inspection uncovers problems, contact a chimney sweep or a qualified repair company to fix the problem before you use the fireplace.

Permanently seal off unused flue openings. Don't use rags or snap-in flue covers.

Check the flues of your gas water heater or furnace for corrosion and obstructions that could present fire hazards.

You may not be able to stop a determined arsonist... but don't make it easier for him.

9. Arson

It may surprise you to learn that arson causes more property damage than any other kind of home fire.

You may not be able to stop a determined arsonist... but don't make it easier for him. Most fires are set from outside the home. A pile of trash or a can of gasoline left in plain sight outdoors not only makes the arsonist's job easier, it might even attract him.

This chapter includes a wealth of facts about how fires start and how they can be prevented. The next chapter gives some specific suggestions for putting this knowledge to use.

CHAPTER

7

Firesafe Living

Twice a year, make a tour of your home with firesafety on your mind. In fact, you can make your first tour now, while you are reading this chapter.

Does your home measure up to firesafety standards from basement to attic? Don't answer before you've made the tour.

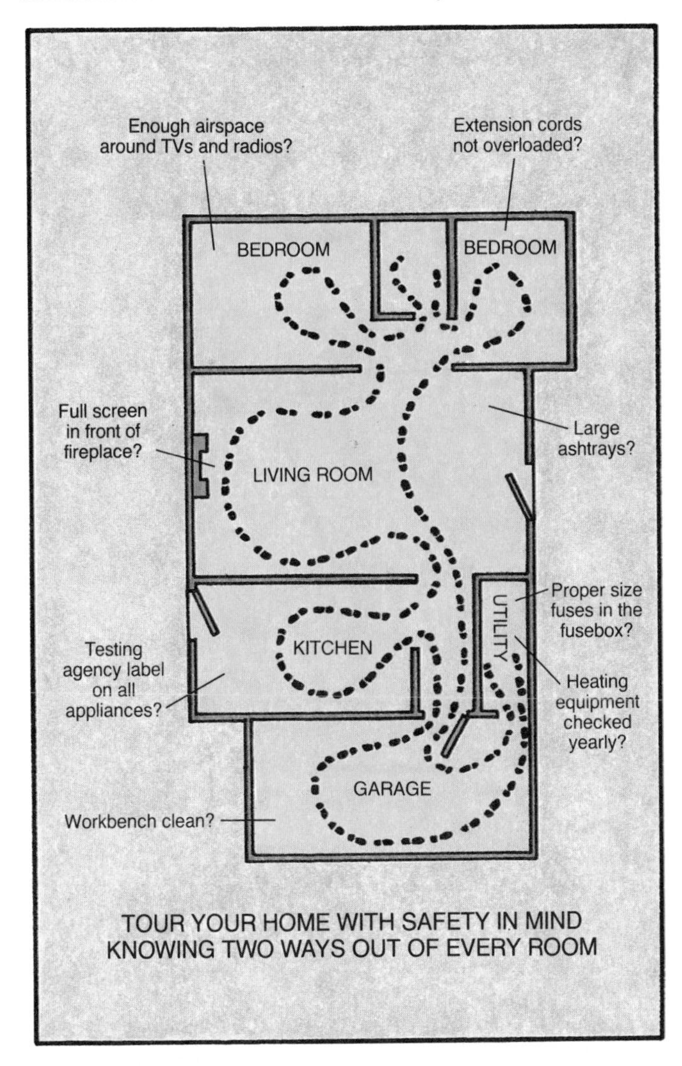

Basement, utility or storage room. Has your heating equipment been checked this year? If there is a fuse box, is it equipped with proper sized fuses, including spares? Is there trash that could fuel a fire? What about sawdust and wood shavings around the work bench? Is the area around the furnace or water heater clear of combustibles?

Garage. If there's gasoline here, is it stored in a safety can? Make sure all flammable liquids are stored here, away from any source of sparks or heat, and not in a basement where a furnace or water heater could ignite flammable vapors.

UNSAFE
Fuzzy, lightweight, loose fabric

Kitchen. Are all appliances in proper working order? If not, don't use them until they're repaired. Do they all have testing laboratory labels? Are outlets overloaded? That's a serious fire hazard.

Living and family room. Are large, stable ashtrays available for smokers? Is the fireplace covered by a sturdy screen of metal or tempered glass? Is there enough air space around stereos and TVs to prevent overheating? Are portable heaters placed away from combustibles, and away from doorways and other traffic paths?

Bedrooms. Is there sufficient air space around appliances? If a smoker uses this room, is there a large ashtray for smoking in a chair (NOT in bed)? Check for overloaded outlets and misused extension cords.

Everywhere. Are there any matches or lighters left where children can reach them? Check for broken wall switches and missing cover plates on switches and electrical outlets.

And how long has it been since you tested and cleaned your smoke detectors? Test them now, and make a note to make that a weekly habit.

SAFE
Sturdy, tightly woven fabric

Plastics and fabrics

Fabrics around your house require special attention, especially in sleepwear for children. Most fabrics will burn with relative ease. And when clothing burns, you burn. Fuzzy, lightweight, loosely woven and loose fitting fabrics burn easily. Denim and wool are less likely to burn quickly.

Sleepwear for children up to 12 years old must be labeled with information on its fire-retardant characteristics. Follow the laundry instructions with these garments, or you may wash out the fire retardants.

Sleepwear for children up to 12 years old must be labeled with information on its fire-retardant characteristics.

Take special care to keep plastics away from heat. While most household plastics do not ignite easily, some plastics emit extremely toxic gases when they burn or smolder.

Special occasions

Don't let fun turn to tragedy. Be alert to the special hazards of camping, outdoor activities and holidays.

Camping. Never have a flame inside a tent: no oil lamps, candles, matches, heaters, or stoves. Use a flashlight inside your tent. When buying tents and sleeping bags, make sure they are labeled "fire retardant." Even so, pitch the tent a safe distance upwind of your campfire.

Have an adult be responsible for matches and lighters; keep them out of children's hands.

Barbecuing. Barbecue grills are deadly hazards indoors, not only because of the fire danger, but because smoldering charcoal produces toxic gases. Outdoors, keep the barbecue a good distance from the house and other combustibles and never leave the fire unattended.

CAUTION: Gasoline is highly flammable and dangerous.

Many people have been severely burned using gasoline to start barbecue fires. Use proper liquid charcoal starter, and do not add any liquid after the fire has started. If the fire burns too low, use dry kindling or blow gently across the coals to revive it.

When you are through cooking, make sure the coals are cool before you leave the barbecue. If you're in a hurry, douse the coals with water.

Gasoline-powered machines. Lawnmowers, motor bikes, chainsaws, snowblowers, garden tractors... all these useful machines present the special danger of handling gasoline. A single spark can ignite gasoline vapors, causing fire and explosion.

Before refueling, always let the engine cool. After filling the tank, move the machine away from the gasoline fumes before starting the engine.

If you must carry gasoline from service station to home, use an airtight, unvented can filled only three-quarters full.

Gasoline is powerful, and its fumes are extremely dangerous. Please don't take the risk of using it for cleaning.

Fourth of July, Mardi Gras, and other holidays. Fireworks are fun and dangerous. Losing your sight or losing a finger is a tragic price to pay for a few minutes' fun with fireworks. To keep your holiday from turning into a tragedy, leave fireworks to professionals, who take extensive safety precautions when producing their spectacular displays.

To keep your holiday from turning into a tragedy, leave fireworks to professionals.

Even seemingly harmless sparklers cause many injuries. Fascinated by the bright sparks, little children are likely to wrap their hands around a stick of fire that may be as hot as 1800 degrees F.

Halloween. Simple precautions can protect your little ghosts and goblins.

In making your own costumes, avoid using flimsy materials, voluminous amounts of old sheets, or paper. These can ignite easily.

When buying ready-made costumes, masks and wigs, make sure they're labeled "flameproof." Don't buy them if they're not.

Use flashlights instead of candles in pumpkins.

Be extra careful with decorations for Halloween and Thanksgiving, many of which are dried and burn easily. Keep them away from fireplaces and other sources of heat, and don't let them block doors or stairs.

Christmas and Hanukkah. These joyous holidays regularly bring an increase in home fires. Let extra caution become a holiday tradition in your family.

Let extra caution become a holiday tradition in your family.

Be especially careful with candles. Don't put them on the tree or on a window sill, or any place where children can get to them. Blow them out when you leave the room.

Buy a fresh tree that is not shedding its needles. After trimming one inch off the bottom, put it in a stable stand, located away from sources of heat and clear of exits. Keep it watered at all times.

If you buy an artificial tree, make sure it is labeled as flame-retardant. Read all warnings carefully, especially about use of lights. Never put electric lights on a metal tree – that's a serious fire and shock hazard.

If your old set of lights is worn or has loose connections, replace it this year. When shopping for lights, look for a testing laboratory's label. Outdoors, use lights specially insulated for outdoor use.

And always unplug everything before your go to bed or leave the house.

Use your fireplace with care (as you should all year round), with a special eye on children. Keep your fireplace screen in place, and don't burn gift wrapping in the fireplace: bits of flaming paper can fly up the chimney and start a roof or chimney fire.

Toys can also be a fire hazard; choose them carefully. Make sure electric toys are labeled for firesafety. If possible, avoid toys that burn easily or use flammable liquids; but if you do choose such toys, recognize their special hazards and use them safely.

Party Safely. Wherever possible, use decorations that are flame-retardant or non-combustible. If people will be smoking, provide large, deep ashtrays, away from your tree and decorations. And before you go to bed, check for misplaced smoking materials, especially under cushions of upholstered furniture.

Make sure no one has left matches or lighters within reach of children who may wake up before you do.

Building firesafety into your home

Whenever you are building, remodeling or expanding your home, you have a chance to make a lasting difference in the firesafety of your family. Buy your materials with firesafety in mind.

Walls – gypsum drywall board offers considerable fire resistance.

Paneling – Look for a fire retardant paneling with a label that gives the flame-spread rating (the lower the rating, the better). In new construction, have a layer of 1/2" gypsum board between paneling and insulation.

Ceiling – Read labels carefully and buy only ceiling tiles that have the label of a testing laboratory.

Insulation – Before installing insulation, check your home's electrical system for any problems. Be sure not to pile up insulation around recessed lighting fixtures: keep insulation 3 inches away to avoid heat build-up. Again, look for the seal of a testing laboratory and check the flame-spread rating of the insulation you buy. (The lower the flame-spread rating, the more firesafe the insulation.)

Alternative heating – If you install factory-built fireplaces or wood stoves to lower your heating bills, be careful and firesafe in selection, installation and maintenance.

The lower the flame-spread rating, the more firesafe the insulation.

When buying a wood stove, look for sturdy construction of cast iron or heavy steel, the label of a testing laboratory, and a damper to control the draft. Beware of danger signs such as cracks or punctures.

Observe the required clearances between the stove and walls or ceiling – as given in the manufacturer's instructions and local safety codes. Minimum clearance is 3 feet but may vary depending on the stove and protective covering on walls.

Usually, 24-gauge steel or 4-inch hollow tile or brick is required as a floor covering under the stove.

Any alternative heating system should be professionally installed or, at a minimum, inspected by a qualified professional before being used.

The many examples in these last two chapters may make it seem that fire hazards are all around us. Fortunately, you have a lot of help these days in being firesafe. Testing laboratories' labels, fire-retardant building materials, decorations, and fabrics – these make it easier to prevent fires in your home.

Still, the best method of fire prevention is being well informed: informed about fire hazards and alert to places where oxygen, fuel and heat may come together to produce a dangerous fire.

CHAPTER

8

When You're on the Spot

If you see a fire start and you are close enough to put it out, a fire extinguisher may keep a small fire from becoming a big one. But you should read this chapter carefully so that you will not endanger yourself by trying to fight a fire with the wrong equipment.

Extinguishers have their limits

A portable fire extinguisher can save lives and property by putting out a small fire or containing it until the fire department arrives.

Portable extinguishers, however, are not designed to fight a large or spreading fire. Even against small fires, they are useful only under the right conditions:

- An extinguisher must be large enough for the fire at hand. It must be available and in working order, fully charged.
- The operator must know how to use the extinguisher quickly, without taking time to read directions during an emergency.
- The operator must be strong enough to lift and operate the extinguisher.

Your extinguisher must fit the fire

Different types of extinguishers are designed for different types of fires.

TYPE A: Ordinary combustibles.
Wood, cloth, paper, rubber, many plastics, and other common materials that burn easily.

ORDINARY COMBUSTIBLES

TYPE B: Flammable liquids.
Gasoline and other flammable liquids, oil, grease, tar, oil-based paint, lacquer and flammable gas.

FLAMMABLE LIQUIDS

TYPE C: Electrical equipment.
Energized electrical equipment, including wiring, fuse boxes, circuit breakers, machinery and appliances.

ELECTRICAL EQUIPMENT

Using an extinguisher that's not rated for the fire you are fighting may make the fire worse! It is particularly dangerous to use water or a Type A extinguisher on a grease or electrical fire.

Multipurpose extinguishers are rated for more than one type of fire. An ABC extinguisher puts out most types of fires that could start in your home— wood, paper, cloth, flammable liquid and electrical fires.

Buy extinguishers carefully

A fire extinguisher should be "listed" or "labeled" by an independent testing laboratory.

The higher the rating number on an A or B extinguisher, the more fire it can put out. But high-rated units are often the heavier models. Make sure you can hold and operate the extinguisher you are buying.

Each extinguisher should be installed in plain view near an escape route.

Remember that extinguishers need care and must be recharged after every use. A partially discharged unit might as well be empty. Ask your dealer how your extinguisher is to be serviced and inspected.

Disposable fire extinguishers can be used only once. Then they must be replaced.

You may need more than one extinguisher. In your home, for example, you may want an extinguisher in the kitchen as well as one in the garage or workshop.

Each extinguisher should be installed in plain view near an escape route and away from potential fire hazards such as heating appliances. Ask your local fire department for advice on the best locations.

Many departments also offer training and practice in use of portable fire extinguishers.

Should you fight the fire?

Before you consider fighting a fire...

1. Make sure everyone has left the building or is leaving.
2. Make sure the fire department has been called.

Never fight a fire if *even one* of the following is true:

...if the fire is spreading beyond the immediate area where it started, or is already a large fire.

...if the fire could block your escape route.

...if you are unsure of the proper operation of the extinguisher.

...if you are in doubt that the extinguisher you are holding is designed for the type of fire at hand or is large enough to fight the fire.

It is reckless to fight a fire with an extinguisher in any one of these cases. Instead, leave immediately, close off the area, and leave the fire to the fire department.

If you do fight the fire, remember the word PASS:

PULL the pin.... Some extinguishers require releasing a lock latch, pressing a puncture lever, or other motion.

AIM low... pointing the extinguisher nozzle (or its horn or hose) at the base of the fire.

SQUEEZE the handle.... This releases the extinguishing agent.

SWEEP from side to side... at the base of the fire until it appears to be out. Watch the fire area. If fire breaks out again, repeat use of the extinguisher.

Most portable extinguishers work according to these directions, but some do not. Read and follow the directions on your extinguisher— on each one if you have more than one make or model.

Protect yourself at all times! Stay low. Avoid breathing the heated smoke and fumes or the extinguishing agent.

If the fire starts to spread or threatens your escape route, get out immediately.

Fighting a fire with water

An ordinary garden hose can aid in extinguishing or containing a small fire in your home, under the conditions described above. But you should never use a hose on an electrical, grease or oil fire.

A garden hose at least 1/2" in diameter and equipped with an adjustable nozzle is a good choice. The hose must be long enough to reach the potential fire area.

To be effective, a hose must remain connected to the water supply at all times, must be checked regularly for deterioration, and must be used only in fire emergencies.

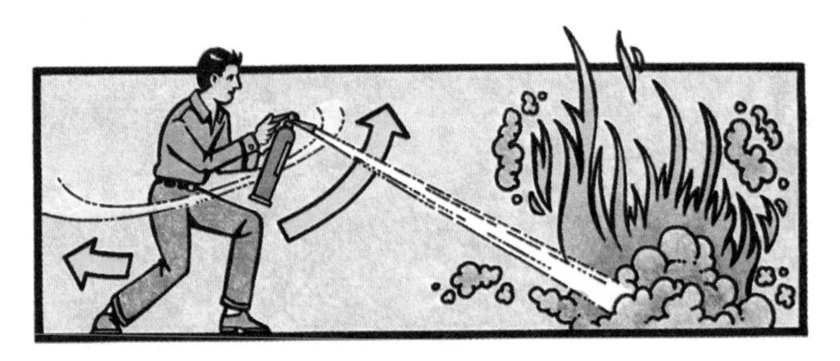

Fight the fire only after the fire department has been called, and only if you can fight it with your back to an exit.

As with a fire extinguisher, aim the hose at the base of the fire, using a side-to-side sweeping motion.

And as with an extinguisher, fight the fire only after the fire department has been called, and only if you can fight it with your back to an exit. If the fire starts to spread or threatens your escape route, leave immediately, close the door behind you and let the fire department handle it.

Individual efforts really do prevent fires and save lives.

A Final Word

The information in this book could save your family's life... but only if you invest the time in planning for firesafety.

For further guidance, call your local fire department. Fire fighters are a concerned and knowledgeable source of information. They put out fires, but they are also dedicated to preventing them.

You can also write directly to the Public Affairs Division of the National Fire Protection Association (NFPA) at Batterymarch Park, Quincy, Massachusetts 02269.

Founded in 1896, NFPA is the only worldwide group dedicated to protection of man and his environment from fire, through education and science.

The Association develops and updates firesafety codes and standards. Thanks to NFPA's reputation for accuracy and integrity, many of these codes and standards have been adopted into federal, state and local law and may be protecting you right now.

Drawing on the largest collection of fire information in the world, NFPA provides technical assistance on all aspects of firesafety, including flammable liquids, electrical safety, nuclear energy, and human safety in buildings.

In addition, NFPA reaches millions of people through its public awareness campaign, which includes Fire Prevention Week and the "Learn Not to Burn" public-service television announcements.

From our national perspective, we see that individual efforts really do prevent fires and save lives. Installing smoke detectors, planning escape routes, and making firesafety checks of your home are effective ways to protect yourself and your family from fire.

We thank you for reading this book. But don't stop here. None of these recommendations will protect you or your family unless you take the time to put them to work.

Now it's up to you.

Home Firesafety Kit

Babysitter Checklist

Cut out this worksheet along the dotted line. Then fill in the blanks and keep the checklist handy for your babysitter. Take the time to tell your babysitter where you will be and how you can be reached. Write that information down.

For more suggestions on firesafety and babysitters, see Chapter 5.

Parents' information for the babysitter:

Names and ages of children: ______________________________

____

____

____

Family name ______________________________

Address ______________________________

Town ______________________________

Home telephone number ______________________________

Fire emergency number ______________________________

Police emergency number ______________________________

Doctor or hospital ______________________________

Poison control center ______________________________

Neighbor's name ______________________________

Neighbor's address ______________________________

Neighbor's telephone number ______________________________

Nearest fire call box ______________________________

Checklist for babysitter:

☐ The doors are locked.

☐ The children are never to be left alone even for a minute.

☐ I know the dangers to children from matches and lighters, gasoline, the stove, deep water, poison, and falls.

☐ I have read the fire escape plan and understand it, including the two escape routes from each room, along with the telephone numbers for use in emergencies.

Fire Escape Plan Grids

Use these grids for creating your family escape plan. Simply cut out this page, draw on it the floor plan of your home, and follow the suggestions in Chapter 3 for marking the various escape routes. See the sample plan on page 15.

When you finish, post the escape plan on a bulletin board or the refrigerator as a constant reminder of the best escape routes in case of fire.

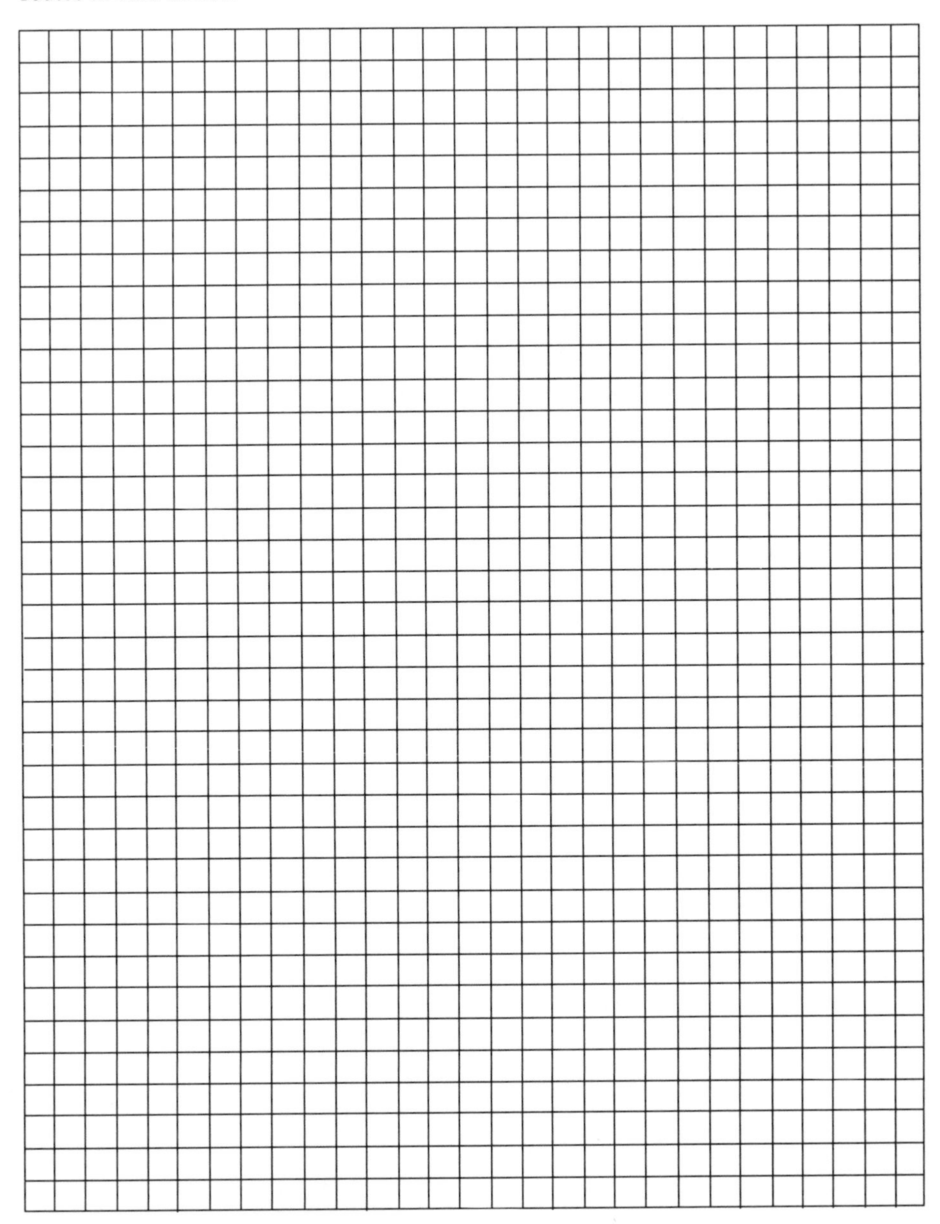

Fire Escape Plan Grids

Use these grids for creating your family escape plan. Simply cut out this page, draw on it the floor plan of your home, and follow the suggestions in Chapter 3 for marking the various escape routes. See the sample plan on page 15.

When you finish, post the escape plan on a bulletin board or the refrigerator as a constant reminder of the best escape routes in case of fire.

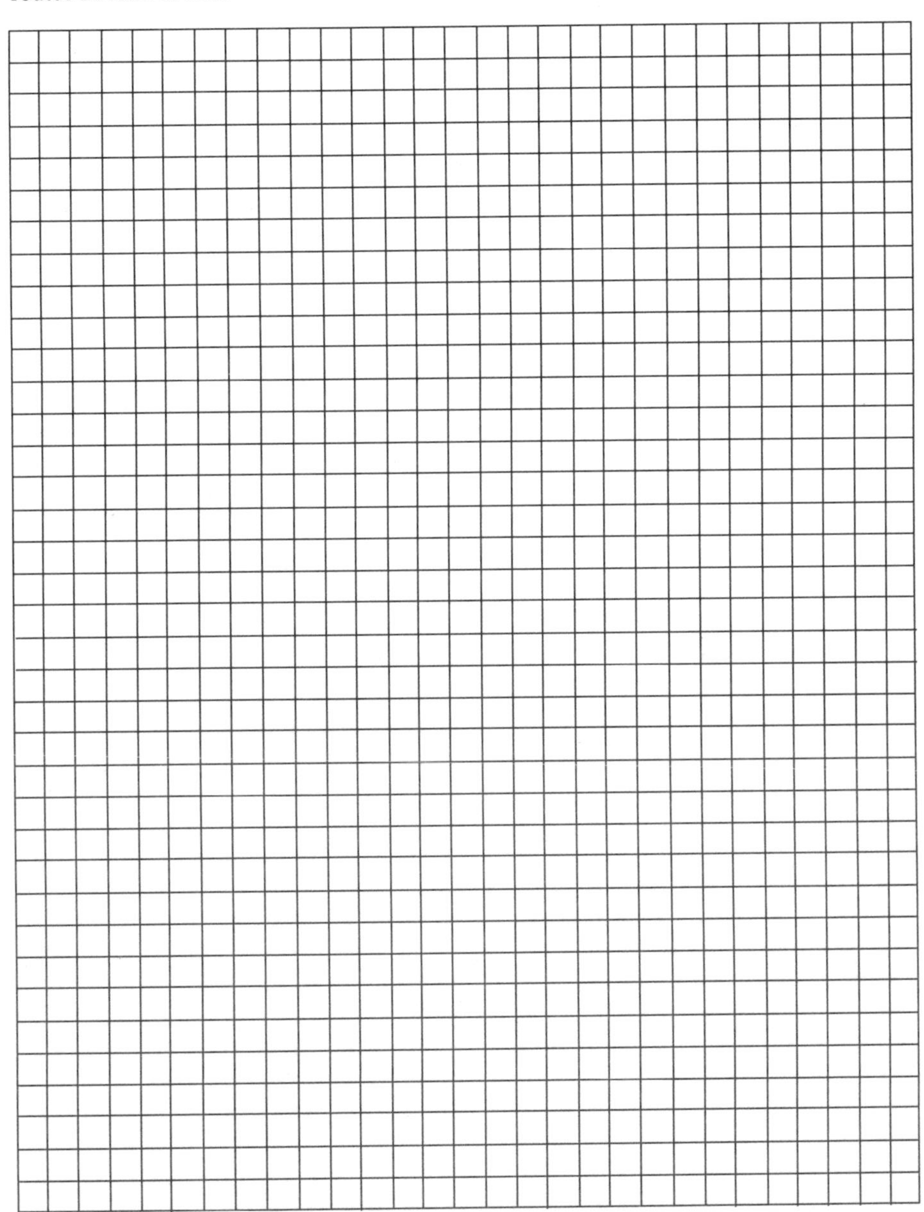